A Second Selection of the

OLD SCOTS
SONGS
WITH
MUSIC

BOOK 2

A SECOND SELECTION OF THE OLD SCOTS SONGS WITH MUSIC

INTRODUCTION

IN this Second Selection of the Old Scots Songs with Music we present a further 22 works including Loch Lomond, Skye Boat Song, Sound the Pibroch, Bonnie Strathyre and Ae Fond Kiss.

The songs are reprinted from three antiquarian sources:—

SONGS OF CALEDONIA, edited by George Eyre-Todd, with pianoforte accompaniments by J Kenyon Lees, and published by Bayley and Ferguson, London and Glasgow.

SONGS OF BURNS with symphonies and accompaniments also by J Kenyon Lees and published by Bayley and Ferguson.

SONGS OF THE NORTH edited by A.C. MacLeod and Harold Boulton with music arranged by Malcolm Lawson. Published by J.B. Cramer, Simpkin Marshall, and Hamilton, Kent and Co.

The introduction in Songs of Burns says: "Among countries remarkable for the extent and beauty of their music Scotland occupies a worthy place. Indeed it would be hard to name any which possesses a richer or more varied Anthology of Song, or one reflecting more faithfully the genius of the country in all its changes and vicissitudes, political and social.

"Every aspect of nature, every social custom, and every stirring deed of arms of which the history of the North Countrie is so full, have been embalmed in imperishable words and allied to music which, whatever its origin, we feel to be instinct with the living fire of inspiration."

Like the songs in our first edition the ones featured in these pages are as popular today as when first written. And in the future they will be played and sung by our children and our children's children . . .

A Second Selection of the Old Scots Songs with Music was published in 1983 by Lang Syne Publishers Ltd., Newtongrange, Midlothian, and printed by Waterside Printers, Old School, Blanefield, Stirlingshire
© LANG SYNE PUBLISHERS LTD.   ISBN No. 946 264 945

Contents of this Book

HO-RO, MY NUT-BROWN MAIDEN.

This fine song, which for long has been one of the best-known lyrics in the Highlands, has within recent years become popular among English singers through two translations, one by Mr. M. Macfarlane of Paisley, printed in Fionn's *Celtic Lyre*, the other by the late Professor John Stuart Blackie. The latter is here given by kind permission of Professor Blackie's executors, Mr. A. W. Blackie and Dr. A. Stodart Walker.

Words translated from the Gaelic by Prof. BLACKIE.

Old Highland Melody.
Sym. and Accomp. by J. Kenyon Lees.

THE WELLS O' WEARIE.

There is a wellknown old ballad, "The Water o' Wearie's Well," in whose various versions some old forgotten story of enchantment and tragedy seems to be shadowed forth. Where exactly the well was to be found, and what were its mystic properties, are points difficult to make out from the ballad. Alexander Ritchie's song, however, which seems to have the same enchanted waters for its subject, affords something more than a hint as to both particulars. The song was printed in the fourth series of *Whistle Binkie* in 1842, and has long been deservedly popular. It is sung to the tune of "The Gypsie Laddie." Still a later song, "The Bonnie Wells o' Wearie," was written by Alexander Maclagan, and set to music by J. C. Grieve. The Wells o' Wearie of the modern song, if not of the old ballad, were long a wellknown trysting place on the side of Arthur's Seat.

Words by *ALEXANDER RITCHIE.*

Air, "*THE GYPSIE LADDIE.*"

Sym. and Accomp. by J. Kenyon Lees.

1. Sweet - ly shines the sun on auld Ed - in - burgh toun, And mak's her look young and cheer - ie, Yet I maun a - wa' to spend the af - ter - noon At the lane - some wells o' Wear - ie. And

2. O the sun win - na blink in thy bon - nie blue e'en, Nor tinge the white brow o' my dear - ie, For I'll big a bow'r wi' rash - es lang and green By the lane - some wells o' Wear - ie. But

you maun gang wi' me, my win-some Ma-ry Grieve; There's
Ma — ry, my love, be - ware ye din - na glow'r At your

nought in the warld to fear ye; For I ha'e asked your min-nie, and
form in the wa-ter sae clear - ly; Or the fai - ry will turn ye in-

she has gi'en ye leave To gang to the wells o' Wear - ie.
to a wee, wee flow'r, And you'll grow by the wells o'

Wear - ie.

THE AULD SCOTS SANGS.

The author of "The Auld Scots Sangs" was of Scottish parentage, but was born in New York about the year 1805. A noted scholar and orator, and a minister of the Dutch Reformed Church, he held charges successively in Utica, Philadelphia, and Brooklyn. Besides several theological works, he wrote and edited *"British Female Poets," "Lays of Love and Faith,"* and Walton's *"Compleat Angler."* He wrote several songs of which that here given is the most famous. Others are to be found in Edwards's *Modern Scottish Poets,* with a biographical notice, from which the above details have been taken. The composer of the air was organist at Arbroath from 1855 till 1857, and died at Dunfermline in 1862.

Air by J. F. LEESON.

Words by the Rev. Dr. BETHUNE.

Scots blood leaps in a' my veins As ye sing the sangs to me,____ And the

Scots blood leaps in a' my veins As ye sing the sangs to me.____

Sing on, sing mair o' thae auld sangs, For

il - ka ane can tell O' joy or sorrow i' the past, Where mem -'ry lo'es to

dwell; Though hair grow grey and limbs grow auld, Un-til the day I dee I'll

bless the Scot-tish tongue that sings The auld Scots sangs to me,____ I'll

bless the Scottish tongue that sings The auld Scots sangs to me.

SOUND THE PIBROCH.

It is interesting that two of the Highland songs best known at the present day should come from the opposite shores of the Sound of Mull. On the Morven shore stands Fiunary, the birthplace of Norman Macleod, senior, and rendered famous by his fine "Farewell." Aros, just opposite, on the shore of Mull, was the native spot of his wife, Agnes Maxwell, who remains almost equally famous as the author of "Sound the Pibroch." Mrs. Macleod lived to see her stalwart and handsome sons among the greatest in Scotland, and only died in 1879, at the age of 93. An account of her early years is to be found in the opening chapter of the "Life of Norman Macleod."

The air and Gaelic refrain of "Sound the Pibroch" were first printed in Alexander Campbell's *Albyn's Anthology* in 1816, the song being entitled "Rise and follow Charlie." The effective final verse of the modern composition was added by the authoress's most famous son, Dr. Norman Macleod.

Words by Mrs. NORMAN MACLEOD, senior.
Last verse by Dr. NORMAN MACLEOD.

Sym. and Accomp. by J. Kenyon Lees.

1. Sound the pibroch loud and high, Frae John o' Groat's to Isle o' Skye! Let a' the clans their slogan cry, And rise and follow Charlie!
2. And see, a small devoted band, By dark Loch Sheil have ta'en their stand, And proudly vow with heart and hand To fight for royal Charlie.
3. Frae ev'ry hill and ev'ry glen Are gath'ring fast the loyal men; They grasp their dirks and shout again, "Hurrah for royal Charlie!"
4. On dark Culloden's field of gore, Hark! hark! they shout, "Claymore! Claymore!" They bravely fight, what can they more? They die for royal Charlie.
5. No more we'll see such deeds again; Deserted is each Highland glen, And lonely cairns are o'er the men Who fought and died for Charlie.

REFRAIN.

Tha tighin fodham, fodham, fodham! *Tha tighin fodham, fodham, fodham—Tha tighin fodham Eirigh!*
(A chin foam, foam, foam! *A chin foam, foam, foam— A chin foam Airie!)*
I must rise and follow, follow! I must rise and follow, follow!— Rise and follow Charlie!

OH, GIN I WERE A BARON'S HEIR.

If, as is sometimes said, it has been impossible in this nineteenth century to write a genuine Scottish ballad—a statement which may well be doubted—it has certainly not been proved impossible to write songs in the genuine spirit of our older minstrelsy. "Oh, gin I were a Baron's heir" might have been sung by a shepherd to his lass among the Lammermuirs or in Douglasdale in the days of Allan Ramsay, or earlier.

Music by J. W. HOLDER.

1. Oh, gin I were a Baron's heir, And could I braid wi' gems your hair, And mak' ye braw as ye are fair, Lass-ie, wad ye lo'e me? And could I tak' ye to the toun, And shaw ye braw sights mony an ane, And busk ye fine in silk-en gown, Lass-ie, wad ye lo'e me?

2. Or should ye be con-tent to prove In low-ly life un-fad-ing love, A heart that nought on earth could move,_ Lass-ie, wad ye lo'e me? And ere the lave-rock wing the sky, Say, wad ye to the for-est hie, And wark wi' me sae mer-ri-ly_ Lass-ie, wad ye lo'e me?

3. And when the fair moon glistens o'er Our wee bit bield and hea-ther muir, Will ye no greet that we're sae puir_ Lass-ie, for I lo'e ye. For I ha'e nocht to of-fer ye, Nae gowd frae mine, nae pearl frae sea, Nor am I come o' high de-gree, Lass-ie, but I lo'e ye.

AE FOND KISS.

2.

I'll ne'er blame my partial fancy,
Naething could resist my Nancy;
But to see her, was to love her;
Love but her, and love for ever.
Had we never lov'd sae kindly,
Had we never lov'd sae blindly,
Never met— or never parted,
We had ne'er been broken hearted.
    Ae fond kiss!

3.

Fare thee weel, thou first and fairest!
Fare thee weel, thou best and dearest!
Thine be ilka joy and treasure,
Peace, enjoyment, love, and pleasure.
Ae fond kiss, and then we sever;
Ae fareweel, alas, for ever!
Deep in heart-wrung tears I'll pledge thee,
Warring sighs and groans I'll wage thee.
    Ae fond kiss!

THE BIRKS OF ABERFELDY.

Bon - nie las - sie, will ye go, will ye go, will ye go,

Bon - nie las - sie, will ye go, to the Birks of A - ber - fel - dy?

1. Now sim - mer blinks on flow'-ry braes, And o'er the cry - stal streamlet plays; Come
2. While o'er their heads the haz - els hing, The lit - tle bird - ies blythe - ly sing, Or

let us spend the light-some days, In the Birks of A - ber - fel - dy.

light - ly flit on wan - ton wing, In the Birks of A - ber - fel - dy.

Bon - nie las - sie, will ye go, will ye go, will ye go,

Bon-nie las-sie, will ye go, to the Birks of A-ber-fel-dy?

3.

The braes ascend like lofty wa's,
The foaming stream deep roaring fa's,
O'erhung wi' fragrant spreading shaws,
    The Birks of Aberfeldy.
      Bonnie lassie, &c.

4.

The hoary cliffs are crown'd wi' flowers,
White o'er the linns the burnie pours,
And rising, weets wi' misty showers
    The Birks of Aberfeldy.
      Bonnie lassie, &c.

5.

Let fortune's gifts at random flee,
They ne'er shall draw a wish frae me,
Supremely blest wi' love and thee,
    In the Birks of Aberfeldy.
      Bonnie lassie, &c.

MY HEART'S IN THE HIGHLANDS.

Tune: "Crochallan."

Slow and with expression.

Doh is F.

|:d .,r |m :r .m |s .m |r :d |d :d .,r |m :s |:d' .,l |

1. My heart's in the High - lands, My heart is not
2. Fare - well to the moun - tains high cov - er'd with
3. Fare - well to the High - lands fare - well to the

|t l :s :l .,s |s f :m :r .,d |d .m :s₁ :s .,f |m :d :r |

here, My heart's in the High-lands, a - chas-ing the
snow; Fare - well to the straths and green val - leys be -
North The birth-place of va - lour the coun - try of

JOHN ANDERSON, MY JO.

Slow, with expression.

Tune: John Anderson my jo.

Voice.

Piano.

Key Bb.

1. John An - der - son my jo, John, When we were first ac -
2. John An - der - son my jo, John, We clamb the hill the -

quent, Your locks were like the ra - ven, Your
gither, And mony a can - ty day, John, We've

THE BONNIE LASS O' BALLOCHMYLE.

Melody by Wm JACKSON.

rang,   A - mang the braes o' Bal - loch-myle,   A - mang the braes o' Bal - loch-
by,   Be - hold the lass o' Bal - loch-myle,   Be - hold the lass o' Bal - loch-

myle,   A - mang the braes o' Bal - loch - myle.   The bon - nie lass! the
myle,   Be - hold the lass o' Bal - loch - myle.

bon-nie, bon-nie lass! The bon-nie lass o' Bal-loch-myle!

Last time

3.

Fair is the morn in flowery May,
     And sweet is night in Autumn mild,
When roving thro' the garden gay,
     Or wandering in a lonely wild:
But Woman, Nature's darling child!
     There all her charms she does compile;
Ev'n there her other works are foil'd
     By the bonnie lass o' Ballochmyle.
       The bonnie lass! &c.

4.

O, had she been a country maid,
     And I the happy country swain,
Tho' shelter'd in the lowest shed
     That ever rose on Scotland's plain!
Thro' weary winter's wind and rain,
     With joy, with rapture, I would toil;
And nightly to my bosom strain
     The bonnie lass o' Ballochmyle.
       The bonnie lass! &c.

AFTON WATER.

Melody by A. HUME.

LOCH LOMOND.

Old Scottish Song.

Traditional Melody arranged by
MALCOLM LAWSON

SKYE BOAT SONG.

*) (JACOBITE.)

Words by
HAROLD BOULTON.

Old Highland rowing measure arranged by
MALCOLM LAWSON.

With animation and well accented.

Chorus to begin, and after each verse.

Speed bon - nie boat like a bird on the wing, on - ward the sai - lors cry; Car - ry the lad that's born to be king

*) This song illustrates an episode in the wanderings of Prince Charlie in the winter of 1745-6, when he made his escape from the net his enemies had spread for him, by putting out to sea with Flora Macdonald and a few devoted Highland boatmen in a rising storm, an example which his pursuers, though well provided with boats, did not venture to imitate.

last time only

SOLO

ff

o - ver the sea to Skye ....

1. Loud the winds howl,
2. Though the waves leap,
3. Ma - ny's the lad
4. Burned are our homes,

loud the waves roar, Thun-der-clouds rend the air;
soft shall ye sleep, O - cean's a roy - al bed.
fought on that day Well the clay - more could wield,
ex - ile and death Scat - ter the loy - al men;

Baff - led our foes stand by the shore, Fol - low they will not dare.
Rocked in the deep Flo - ra will keep Watch by your wea - ry head.
When the night came si - lent - ly lay Dead on Cul - lo - den's field.
Yet ere the sword cool in the sheath Char - lie will come a - gain.

D. C. from the sign

THE COOPER O' FIFE.

Old Lowland Ballad.

Old Lowland air arranged by
MALCOLM LAWSON.

Rather fast, but following the singer.

With humour.   *Coro:*

1. There was a wee coop - er, who liv'd in Fife,   * Nick - e - ty, nack - e - ty,

Solo.

noo,   noo, noo,   And   he   has got - ten   a gen - tle wife;

Coro:

Hey Wil - lie wal - la - chy!   Now   John Dou - gal   a - lane,   Quo rush - e - ty

in time.

* This chorus is often sung in the "Kingdom of Fife" to the accompaniment of one stroke of the elbow on a wooden table, followed by two of the fist — which will be found to be a very good imitation of the noise made by the movement of the shuttle in weaving. Perhaps, with this assistance, the uninitiated will find some elucidation of the meaning of the refrain.

Coro: *Solo.*

Nick - e - ty nack - e - ty noo, noo, noo; He's laid a sheep skin

Nick - e - ty nack - e - ty noo, noo, noo; "And think nae mair o' my

Coro:

on her back; Hey Wil-lie wal - la - chy! Now John Dou-gal a-

gen - tle kin" Hey Wil-lie wal - la - chy! Now John Dou-gal a -

- lane, Quo rush - e - ty roo, roo, roo!

- lane, Quo rush - e - ty roo, roo, roo!

f

3. I'll

4. All

Coro.

Hey, Wil - lie wal - la - chy! Now John Dou - gal a -

- lane, Quo rush - e - ty roo; roo; roo;

LINTEN LOWRIN.

Old Aberdeenshire Song.

Traditional Melody arranged by
MALCOLM LAWSON.

1. sheared my first hairst in Bog - end, Doun by the fit o'
2. Rhy - nie's wark is ill to work, And Rhy - nie's wa - ges
3. Rhy - nie is a Hie - land place, It does - a suit a

Ben - a - chie; And sair I wrought and sair I fought, But
are but sma'; And Rhy - nie's laws are dou - ble straight, And
Law - land loon; And Rhy - nie is a cauld clay hole, It

a little quicker

I wan out my pen - ny fee;
that does grieve me maist of a';
is na like my fai - ther's toun;

rit.   *mf*

Lin - ten low - rin, low - rin lin - ten,

Lin - ten low - rin lin - ten lee: I'll gang the gait I cam' a - gain, And a

f   *rit.*   *a tempo*

D. C. dal Segno

bet - ter bair - nie I will be.

with the voice   *a tempo*   *dim.*

2. O
3. O

AIKEN DRUM

Old political squib.

(Traditional.)

Ancient Lanarkshire Air arranged by

MALCOLM LAWSON.

1. There cam' a man to our toun, to our toun, to our toun, Oh! A
2. And his coat was made o' the gude roast beef, the gude roast beef, the gude roast beef, Oh! His
3. And his breeks were made o' the hag-gis bags, the hag-gis bags, the hag-gis bags, Oh! His
4. And his buttons were made o' the baw-bee baps, the baw-bee baps, the baw-bee baps, Oh! His

queer man cam' to our toun, And they ca'd him Ai-ken Drum.
coat was made o' the gude roast beef, And his name was Ai-ken Drum.
breeks were made o' the hag-gis bags, And they ca'd him Ai-ken Drum.
buttons were made o' the baw-bee baps, And his name was Ai-ken Drum.

THE BUSH ABOON TRAQUAIR.

Words by
Principal SHAIRP.

Music by
HAROLD BOULTON.

THE BONNIE EARL O' MORAY.

Old Scottish Song.

Traditional Melody arranged by
MALCOLM LAWSON.

Sustained and slow.

Voice.

1. Ye
2. O

Heavy and marked

Piano.

Hie - lands and ye Law - lands, O
wae be - tide ye Hunt - ly, And

where hae ye been? They hae
where - fore did ye sae? I...............

"On Feb. 7th, 1592, the Earl of Moray was cruelly murdered by the Earl of Huntly at Dunibrissel in Fifeshire . . .; to satisfy the King's (James VI) jealousy of Moray, whom the Queen more rashly than wisely had commended in the King's hearing with too many epithets of a proper and gallant man". Sir James Balfour's History of Scotland:

BONNIE STRATHYRE.

Words by
HAROLD BOULTON.

Music adapted from old Air "Taymouth"
and arranged by MALCOLM LAWSON.

WILLIE'S GANE TO MELVILLE CASTLE.

Old Scottish Song.

Scottish Air arranged by
MALCOLM LAWSON.

Rather fast and with appropriate humour.

1. O Wil - lie's gane to Mel-ville Cas - tle, Boots and spurs an'
2. The first he met was La - dy Kate, She led him through the
3. Then ben the house cam' La - dy Bell, "Gude troth ye need na
4. When on his horse he rade a - wa', They ga - thered round the

a', To bid the led - dies a' fare - weel Be
ha', And wi' a sad and sor - ry heart She
craw, May - be the lad will fan - cy me And
door, He gai - ly waved his bon - net blue, They

fore he gaed a - wa'.   Wil - lie's young and blithe and bon-nie,
let the tear-drop fa':   Be - side the fire stood La - dy Grace, Said
dis - ap-point ye a'.'   Doun the stair trip - ped La - dy Jean, The
set up sic a roar.   Their cries, their tears brought Wil - lie back, He

rit.

Lo'ed by ane an' a', O! what will all the las - ses do When
ne'er a word a - va; She thocht that she was sure o' him Be -
flower a - mang them a', "O las - ses trust in pro - vi - dence, And
kissed them ane an' a'; "O las - ses bide till I come hame, And

rit.

D.C. dal Segno 𝄋

Wil - lie gaes a - wa'?
fore he gaed a - wa'.
ye'll get hus - bands a'."
then I'll wed ye a'."

rit.   *in time*   *cres.*   *Fine*

D.C. dal Segno 𝄋

SIR PATRICK SPENS.

Music founded on an
Old Northern Air by
MALCOLM LAWSON.

Old Scots Ballad (adapted for singing)

ballad fashion varying the time with the sentiment.

King sits in Dun - ferm - line town, Drinking the blood-red wine: "Oh! Whare will I get a

skeely skip-per To sail this ship o' mine?" Oh! Up and spake an el-dern knight, Sat

at the King's right knee: "Sir Pat - rick Spens is the best sai - lor That

ev-er sail'd the sea;" "To Nor-ro-way, to Nor- ro - way, To Nor- ro-way o'er the

foam, The King's daughter to Nor-ro - way 'Tis thou must bring her home:" "Be it
faem,   hame:"

rit:

cres: *f* *In time.*

wind or weet, Be it hail or sleet, Our ship must sail the foam; The King's daughter to
faem;

rit:

f *In time.*

Nor-ro - way 'Tis we must bring her home, 'tis we must bring her home."
hame,   hame."

8

LEEZIE LINDSAY.

Old Scottish Ballad.

Traditional Air arranged by
MALCOLM LAWSON.

OUR FIRST EDITION FEATURES THE UNDERNOTED SONGS WITH FULL MUSICAL ACCOMPANIMENT

Scots Wha Hae Wi' Wallace Bled

When You and I were young, Maggie

Lochnagar

We Willie Winkie

Bonnie Mary of Argyle

My love is like a red, red rose

Weel may the keel row

The Campbells are comin'

Heiland Laddie

The Deil's awa' wi' the Exciseman

Oh Alister MacAllister

A guid new year to ane an' a'

Johnnie Cope

Bonnie Dundee

Bonnie Wee Thing

O Charlie is My Darling

The Laird O' Cockpen

Auld Lang Syne

Corn Rigs

Jock O' Hazeldean

Annie Lawrie

The Hundred Pipers

Kelvin Grove

Ye Banks and Braes

The Piper O' Dundee

Duncan Gray

A man's a man for a' that

Blue Bonnnets over the Border

The Rowan Tree

Comin' thro' the Rye

Green Grow the Rashes o'

My love she's but a lassie yet

The Jolly Beggar

The Blue Bells of Scotland

Caller Herrin'

The Flowers of the Forest

O, Willie Brew'd a peck o' maut

O'er the muir amang the heather

Available from John Menzies, R.S. McColl, W.H. Smith and good book and craft stores throughout Scotland, or direct from the publishers priced £2.95 plus 55p postage.

MADE IN SCOTLAND